CAN YOU SOLVE THESE?
Mathematical problems to
test your thinking powers.
SERIES No. 3

DAVID WELLS

TARQUIN PUBLICATIONS

Many of the problems in this book first appeared, sometimes in a different form, in issues 7 and 8 of The Problem Solver, written and edited by David Wells.

I should like to thank Adrian Jenkins for providing some elegant new problems as well as improving many of the originals.

Problems 59 and 69 are due to Nobuyuki Yoshigahara, Japan's leading puzzle composer. Problem 100, Cross's Theorem, first appeared in Mathematical Digest No. 58, January 1985.

D. W.

0 906212 53 7
© DAVID WELLS 1986
Editor: ADRIAN JENKINS
Printing: ANCIENT HOUSE PRESS

TARQUIN PUBLICATIONS
STRADBROKE
DISS
NORFOLK IP21 5JP
ENGLAND

An up-to-date catalogue of other Tarquin books may be obtained by writing to the publishers at the address above.

PROBLEM SOLVING

Mathematics is not a spectator sport !

Recent years have seen a blossoming of interest in problem solving. No longer is doing mathematics the province of professionals only. Anyone can join in, exercise their wits and imagination and discover the delight of mathematical ideas. Don't worry if you have forgotten most of the mathematics you ever knew. Ingenuity, perseverance and a flash of insight will be more useful than book-knowledge.

If you get really stuck the HINTS will offer help without giving the solution away. Printed upside down to discourage peeping is a section of SOLUTIONS. These will tell you whether you are right or wrong, usually with a short explanation, while leaving you ample scope to continue your investigation into the problem, or to use it as a starting point for investigations of your own.

Good problem solving !

David Wells

Reading down and across there are eight answers in this cross-number puzzle.

You are given only four clues, plus the fact that no answer begins with a zero.

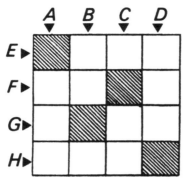

Clues:

D=9E	F=9B
A=H+91	E=C+G

Can you find a point T, somewhere inside this triangle, so that the areas of the three triangles ATB, BTC and CTA are equal ?

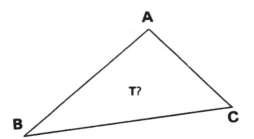

1

WHAT COMES NEXT ?

$2^2 - 0^2 = 4$ $5^2 - 1^2 = 24$
$3^2 - 1^2 = 8$ $6^2 - 2^2 = 32$
$4^2 - 2^2 = 12$ $7^2 - 3^2 = 40$
.... = ... = ...

$3^2 - 0^2 = 9$ $7^2 - 2^2 = 45$
$4^2 - 1^2 = 15$ $8^2 - 3^2 = 55$
$5^2 - 2^2 = 21$ $9^2 - 4^2 = 65$
.... = ... = ...

Here are four patterns of the same type. Each pattern could be
continued indefinitely. Explore patterns of this kind.

4 IS IT A DRAW?

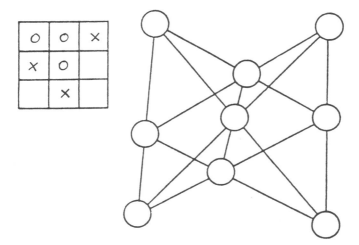

On the left is the usual noughts and crosses board. There are eight ways in which you could get three O's or three X's in a row, but if both players play well the game ought to be a draw.

What about the noughts and crosses board on the right? Here there are 9 ways to get three in a row. What should the result be if both players play well - a draw, or a win for one player?

5 If P, Q, and R are ordinary numbers then it is *always* true that:

$$P \times (Q + R) = (P \times Q) + (P \times R)$$

but it is almost always *not true* that:

$$P + (Q \times R) = (P + Q) \times (P + R)$$

Find an exceptional set of three numbers which *does* make the second statement true.

6 Using a ball as a model of a sphere, find eight points on its surface, so that each of the points is exactly the same distance from three of the other points.

   Does it make a difference whether you measure the distance across the surface of the sphere or in a straight line through it?

7 A strip of paper with a straight edge is bent over the edge of a cube, like this:

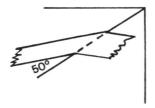

The angle between the strip and the edge on one face of the cube is 50°. What will be the angle between the strip and the edge on the other face of the cube?

8 If each of these three lines divides this area into two equal parts, which is the biggest, area A or area B, or is it not possible to say?

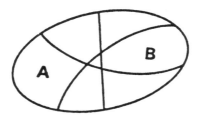

(The diagram is only a rough sketch: it has not been drawn accurately.)

9 Here are two very short coded messages:

T RBU MHCS GDF and **H SJQ REYN TKL**

The codes used for each message are definitely different. Could the original messages be the same? Must they be the same?

 A cube makes a fair 6-valued dice, and a dodecahedron makes a fair 12-valued dice. How could you make a fair 10-valued dice?

 In the left-hand rectangle it is certainly true that $a^2 + b^2 = c^2$. In the right-hand rectangle point T has moved out into the rectangle. Is it now true that:

$$a^2 + b^2 = c^2 + d^2 ?$$

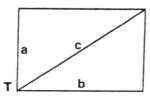 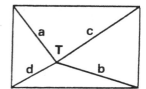

Here are two points, (2,4) and (5,6) marked on a grid of points. When they are joined by a straight line, it does not go through any other grid point.

If (3,8) and (11,18) were marked and joined, would the line go through any other grid points?

Is there a way of telling without actually drawing a grid and marking the points?

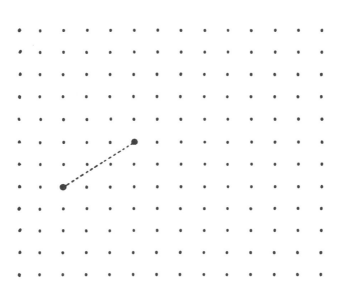

Test your answer on (5,18) and (61,81).

This pattern is made up entirely from squares and equilateral triangles, and it repeats for ever in all directions. However, some pairs of squares are next to each other.

Can you find a tessellation of the same two shapes which never has two squares next to each other?

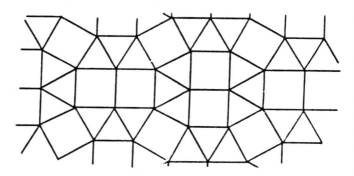

 Can you divide a circle into three equal parts, so that no dividing line passes through the centre? The pieces do not have to be the same shape, but must have the same area.

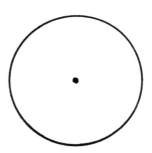

How can two identical squares be cut so that the pieces can be reassembled to make a single larger square?

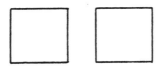

Suppose that the two squares were different sizes. Is it still possible to cut them up so that they can be reassembled to make a single larger square?

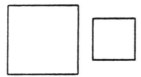

If 'All squifms are norit', and 'Some things which are norit are also meghim', must it also be true that 'Some squifms are meghim'?

$$\text{If } a = b + c$$
$$\text{then } a^2 - b^2 - c^2 = 2bc$$
$$\text{and } a^4 + b^4 + c^4 = 2b^2c^2 + 2c^2a^2 + 2a^2b^2$$

How is it possible for the first, unsymmetrical, equation to turn into the final symmetrical equation?

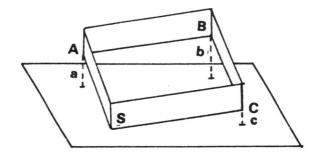

 This rectangular frame has one corner only resting on the table top. Find a connection between the heights a, b, c of the other three corners above the surface of the table.

 There is no number except 1 which divides into all three of these numbers.

125,611   243,986   369,599

How can you prove this statement easily?

 Find or make a cylinder with circular faces at right angles to its axis. Is it possible to divide its curved surface into a grid of squares which completely covers the curved surface, with no gaps, no overlapping, and which goes right up to the edges?

21

Line

1	C B C C B A C A
2	A A C A C B B
3	A B B B A B
4	C B B C C
5	A B A C
6	C C B
7	C A
8	B

This pattern is formed by using very simple rules.

1   Start in line 1 with any sequence of the letters A, B, C in any order.
2   If neighbouring letters are different, place the third letter beneath and between.
3   If neighbouring letters are the same, place the same letter beneath and between.
4   Continue until you end with a single letter.

The problem is to discover if you can work out any lower lines, without filling in the intermediate steps first. For instance, is it possible to write down line 7 without working out lines 2, 3, 4, 5, 6 first?

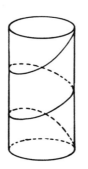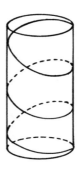

22

Two helices are drawn on a cylinder. (A helix is a spiral which rises up the cylinder at a steady rate.) One helix goes from top to bottom in two complete turns, clockwise, while the other goes from top to bottom in three complete turns, anti-clockwise. Both start at the same point.

How many different areas is the surface of the cylinder divided into by the two spirals?

23

Mark a point X anywhere inside a closed convex curve.
 Is it *always* possible to find two points, both on the curve, such that X is the middle point of the line joining them?

```
482     282
153      47
        ───
        329
```

The working above shows a method of subtracting 153 from 482. The answer of 329 appears beneath the line on the right.

How does this method of subtraction work?

25

Four non-zero digits placed in these four squares will make two numbers across and two numbers down.

If the sum of the four numbers is 67, what are they?

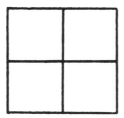

CODEBREAKING

To break an unknown code usually needs a very long message. However, with some clues, it is possible to solve even just a few words.

These three sets of words are written in three different codes.

1 Are the members of this pair equal?

PZJZAFSFZ
ZABSFTF

2 What about this family?

ABCADE
EDDBFGE
HIFECJKAL
FLCLJKDL

3 It needs solid thought to decode these!

MNOPQRNSPTU
TVWQRNSPTU
RNXQRNSPTU
STSNVQRNSPTU
YVTZQRNSPTU

27 Imagine that a circle is divided into several equally spaced slices, as in the upper diagram. The dividing lines are then tilted to point in another direction, as on the lower diagram. Investigate the shape formed by their ends.

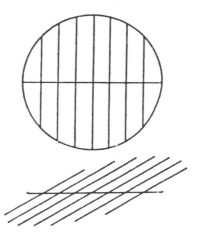

28 Explain how you could construct an accurate square on the surface of a cone.

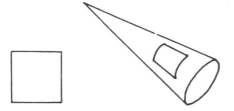

29

Fit six of the first shape together, to make the second:

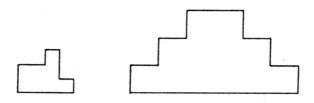

30

In 3-dimensional space it is always possible to imagine a plane through any three given points. However, four points chosen at random do *not* usually lie in any plane.

Do these points lie in a plane: (4,1,6), (5,2,8), (7,5,8) and (8,4,11)?

31

Find n points on the surface of a sphere such that every one of the n points is equidistant from the 4 other nearest points in the set. For what values of n does this problem have a solution?

32

Can this pattern be continued for ever in all directions? How can you be sure?

This is a prism with five faces, plus two end-faces, making 7 faces in total.

How many other polyhedra can you discover or invent which also have 7 faces?

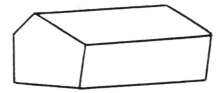

The number 12 belongs to a certain class of special numbers. It has factors 1, 2, 3, 4, 6 and the sum of three of those factors, $2 + 4 + 6$ is equal to 12. Find other numbers where the sum of exactly three of its factors add up to the number itself. What is the connection between them and why can there be no others?

The number 17^{19} is very large. Without working it out can you answer the question:

Is 17^{19} divisible by 7?

36 If you draw a loop on a flat surface, like this, it divides the surface into an inside and an outside. You can only get from the inside to the outside by crossing the loop.

Can you find an object at home on which you can draw a loop which does NOT divide the surface into an inside and an outside?

37

To make a rectangle balance on a pin you must place the point under the centre of the rectangle. Where must you place the point to balance a shape made out of two rectangles together, like this?

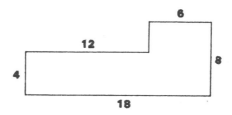

38 It is not difficult to prove that the sum of the fractions

$$1/2, 1/4, 1/8, 1/16, 1/32 \ldots$$

taken on for ever is 1.
Can you construct a sequence of these fractions so that when taken on for ever the sum is $1/3$?

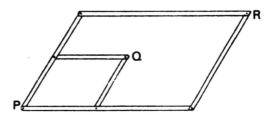

This figure shows six strips fitted together with pins to make two parallelograms, one inside the other.

The two shorter strips form a parallelogram similar in shape to the larger one.

If the corner P does not move, how does Q move when R is moved to trace out a shape?

However much a pack of ordinary cards is shuffled, there is a chance that when they are dealt out, one at a time, face up, there will be a long run of black or red. For example, there might be seven blacks in a row.

Experiment with a mini-pack of six cards, three of each colour. What is the chance that after shuffling them well they will deal out **black-black-black-red-red-red**?

If you are given that $a + b = 1$ and $a^2 + b^2 = 1$, what is the value of $a^5 + b^5$?

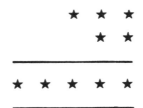

This is a multiplication sum where each digit is represented by a ★. None of the digits is zero. If the five digit answer is as small as possible, what are the two and three digit numbers?

Draw a line and on it mark off a length which can be called "1 unit".

$$\underline{\qquad\qquad \overset{\textstyle 1 \text{ unit}}{\underset{\textstyle |\qquad\quad|}{}} \qquad\qquad}$$

Using ruler and compasses only construct lengths of
$\sqrt{5}$, $\sqrt{29}$, $\sqrt{35}$ and $\sqrt{33}$ units.

448 and 441 are multiples of 56 and 63 respectively. 448 − 441 = 7 and 7 happens to be the highest common factor of 56 and 63.

Prove that for any pair of numbers, it is always possible to find two multiples which differ by their highest common factor.

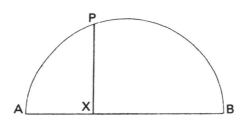

This is half a circle. PX is at right-angles to the diameter AB. Investigate the relationship between the lengths AX, BX and PX.

How many items of information are needed to describe the position of a straight line on a graph, if the axes and their scales are already drawn?

WHAT NUMBER AM I?

I am equal to the sum of the cubes of my own digits. I am the sum of consecutive factorials and I am triangular. I am also, according to the New Testament, the number of fishes caught by the apostle Simon Peter. What am I?

On the straights before and after the corner, the cars are equally spaced and travelling at 60kph. What would you estimate is the speed of the cars round the corner?

Why is the product of any four consecutive integers never a perfect square?

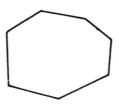

"A polygon is convex", said Mary,"if the straight line segment joining any two points on its edge lies entirely inside the polygon".
"It is also convex", remarked Peter, "if no vertex lies inside the triangle formed by any three other vertices".
Mary's definition is the usual one. Is Peter's definition really equivalent?

This shape, seen here from two different directions, is made up from four identical cubes, three of them attached to three faces of the fourth.

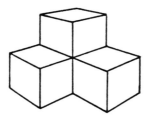

Is it possible to fill the whole of space with an infinite number of these shapes, without leaving any spaces or gaps?

How long is the middle rung of this fruit picking ladder? The rungs are equally spaced vertically.

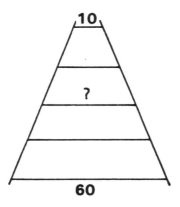

10

?

60

Use a calculator or a computer to find which two numbers less than 100 are such that the sum of their square roots is closest to a whole number. The numbers must not be perfect squares themselves.

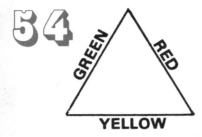

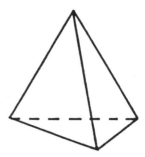

The edges of the triangle have been marked with the colours, red, yellow and green in clockwise order. It does not matter where you start.

Is it possible to colour all the edges of a tetrahedron with the same three colours, so that the colours arranged around each triangular face are in the same clockwise order?

The six digits 1, 2, 4, 5, 7, 8 may be separated into two groups of three or three groups of two while maintaining their order. The groups can then be added

$$124 + 578 = 702$$
$$12 + 45 + 78 = 135$$

Can you rearrange the same six digits so that when separated and added in the same way, the totals are 999 and 99?

When is the average of the averages of two sets of numbers equal to the average of all the numbers taken together?

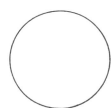
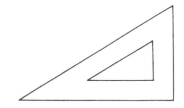

You are given a circle with nothing marked on it or in it.
How can you find its centre using only a set square?

You are shown four points marked on a piece of paper and you are told that they are the corners of a square.
How many measurements would you have to make to make certain that this was true?

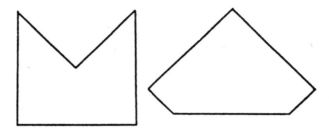

Cut the first shape into just two pieces which can be fitted together to make the second shape.

 WHAT NUMBER AM I?

I am the area and the perimeter of a certain right-angled triangle. I am the largest number, such that all those numbers less than me which do not share a common factor with me are prime. I am the number of edges of two well-known polyhedra. What number am I?

61

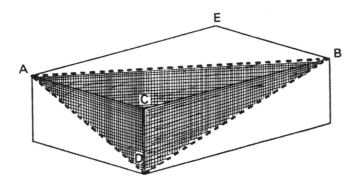

What fraction of the volume of the whole box is the tetrahedron ABCD?

If the box is made of thin card and the tetrahedron is cut away, what fraction of its original weight still remains?

Mark three points on a piece of paper, for example like this. How many points can you find which are the *same* distance from each of these three points?

Suppose you started with three straight lines: how many points could you find which were the same distance from each of the three lines?

• •

•

There is only one pair of integers such that

$$p^q = q^p$$

Can you find them and prove that there are no others?

If

$$(p^q)^r = p^{q^r}$$

What are the possible values of p, q, r, if they are known to be integers.

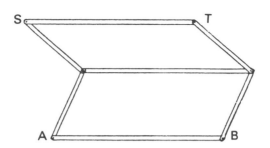

This figure shows seven strips making two parallelograms with a shared edge.

If the bottom edge AB does not move, how does S move compared to T?

2 White
3 Black

3 White
4 Black

Two identical bags contain different numbers of white and black counters.

A bag is chosen at random and a single counter removed from it. The counter was white.

What was the probability that the bag which was chosen was bag A?

67

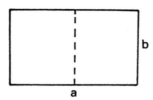

It was found that when a certain rectangular piece of paper was cut in half that each half was in the same proportion as the original. What proportions must the original have had?

68

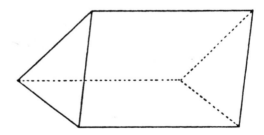

Is it possible to cut this prism into three tetrahedra which all have the same volume, even if their shapes are different?

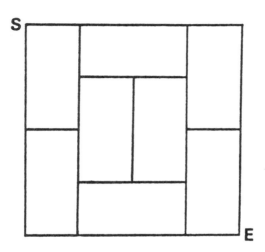

You have to move from the START marked 'S' to the END marked 'E'.

What is the *longest* possible route, if you are not allowed to travel along any line more than once.

70

"If the sum of two numbers is 1001, then their product is not divisible by 1001".

True or false? And why?

71

A pair of scissors is either right or left-handed, with most pairs on sale being right-handed. Examine a pair and determine how the handedness of a pair of scissors can be identified.

72 The equation

$$t^2 - 5t + 7 = 0$$

has two distinct roots. Call them a and b.

Prove that a + b = 5 *without* solving the equation first.

This figure shows four identical right-angled triangles on the sides of a square. Two of them are facing inwards and two outwards.

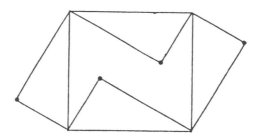

Why do the four vertices marked with dots lie in a straight line?

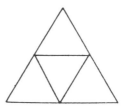

Here is an equilateral triangle cut into four other smaller equilateral triangles. Is it possible to dissect it into six smaller equilateral triangles? They do not have to be all the same size.

What numbers of equilateral triangles is it *NOT* possible to dissect it into?

75

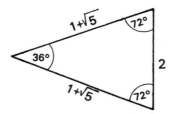

An isosceles triangle with angles of 36°, 72°, 72° has its unequal sides in the ratio of 2 : 1 + √5.

Use this fact to construct a regular pentagon using only a straight edge and compasses, as efficiently as possible.

76

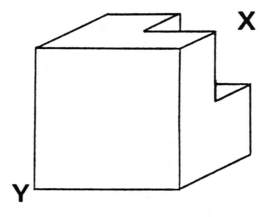

This is a 2 x 2 x 2 cube with a 1 x 1 x 1 cube removed from one corner. What shape would you see if you looked at the damaged cube along the diagonal from the corner X which is now missing towards the opposite corner Y?

77

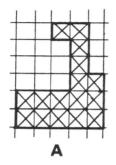 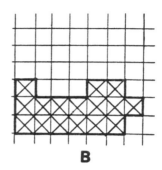

A   **B**

Shape A is made up of two pieces, one of which is the mirror image of the other.

Shape B is made up of four identical pieces

Can you find the shapes of the pieces?

78

X is an integer. There is only one value of X where X^7 and X^{13} contain 38 digits between them. What is X?

A knight's tour on a chess board is the path taken by a knight as it travels the board visiting any square only once.

Show that it is impossible for a knight to do a tour of a 5 x 5 board and then return to its starting point.

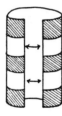

If the 5 x 5 chess board is rolled into a cylinder, does it then become possible to complete the knight's tour?

On the original flat board is it possible to make a knight's tour that visits every square exactly once, but does not return to its starting point?

How can two straight roads be constructed across this rectangular area, so that the maximum distance of any point in the rectangle from one of the roads is as small as possible?

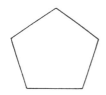

How could two straight roads be drawn across this regular pentagon, under the same conditions?

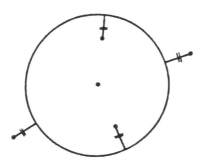

In the diagram, a circle has been constucted so that its circumference is equidistant from four given points.

Show that this is always possible for any 4 points, provided that all 4 of them do not lie on a straight line.

82

```
C  A  C  B
   B  B  A  A
      B  C  A  C
         A  B  B  A
            C  B  C  A
               A  A  B  B
                  A  C  B  C
                     B  A  A  B
                        C  A  C  B
```

This pattern as been produced by the same rules as the pattern in Problem 21. The additional letter on the right is obtained by applying the same rules to the first and last letters of the line above.

After 8 lines, the pattern repeats itself and would continue for ever, with a repetition every 8 lines. Is it true that every pattern will repeat itself in this way after a certain number of lines?

(3,4) and (7,10) are the
ends of one diagonal of
a square, on a square grid.
What are the ends of the
other diagonal? can you
find out without drawing
it on graph paper?

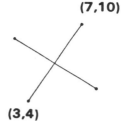

(7,10)

(3,4)

The decimal period of the fraction $1/7$ is six digits long.

$$1/7 = 0 \cdot \overline{142857}142857......$$

What is the smallest number whose reciprocal has a decimal
period of length 7?

The sum of the opposite sides of a cubical die is 7. There are
only two ways of numbering an ordinary die to achieve this.

How many ways are there of numbering an octahedral die?
It has 8 faces, so the total of each pair of opposite faces will be 9.

What about a dodecahedral die?

KNIGHT'S SQUARE

1	2	3	4
5	6	7	8
9	10	11	12
13	14	15	16

A

16	12	8	4
15	11	7	3
14	10	6	2
13	9	5	1

B

The aim of this puzzle is to rearrange the numbers 1 to 16 using a series of swaps.

A swap can take place between the numbers in any two squares which are related by a knight's move in chess.

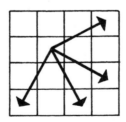

Can it be done?

The diagram below shows two similar triangles. Your tricky task is to construct, using ruler and compasses only, another triangle of whatever shape you choose, whose area is equal to the sum of the areas of the two given triangles.

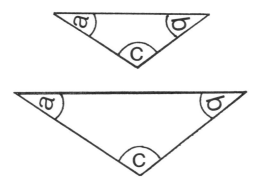

Hint: Regard each triangle as half a parallelogram and then work with the parallelograms.

Copies of a magazine cost 60p each. There is, however, a discount for bulk orders. If 30 or more copies are ordered, the price is 50p each.

What quantities of the magazine are never worth ordering?

Colour the 15 balls in this snooker triangle so that 5 are red, 5 yellow and 5 green in such a way that the smallest distance between any two balls of the same colour is as great as possible.

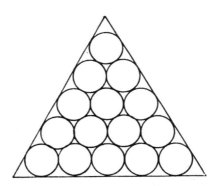

AB is a fixed line. The point P moves in space so that the angle APB stays constant.

What shape does P trace out?

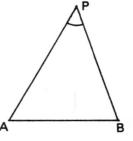

NUMBERS AS LETTERS
OR LETTERS AS NUMBERS

Continue this sequence

1, 4, 3, 11, 15, 13, 17, ...

This is part of a tessellation made from just one shape of irregular quadrilateral, repeated endlessly. Can you construct a tessellation which uses equal numbers of four different irregular quadrilaterals?

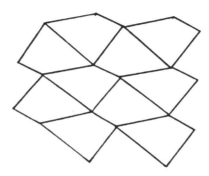

If a tap is turned on gently to give a continuous stream of water, the falling column tapers as it falls.

Explain why this is.

What is the width of the column related to?

45

Many variations on Rubik's cube have been invented. Some are more complicated than the original, others are simpler. This is one of the simplest variations.

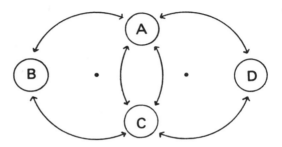

Four pieces are arranged in two rings of three pieces each. There are four possible moves, the pieces in either ring may be rotated one place each either clockwise or anticlockwise.

Solve this puzzle completely by finding every possible position which can be reached, and by showing the relationship between them as a graph or network.

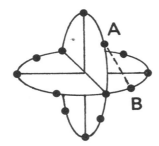

Two circles have the same centre and the same radius of 10cm. Their planes are at right angles. Each circumference is divided into eight equal parts. Calculate AB.

THINKING OF TWO?

What are the next numbers in each sequence?

(a) 1, 1, 3, 5, 11, 21, 43, . . .
(b) 3, 5, 6, 9, 10, 12, . . .

234,765

In this number you may notice that the two 'halves', 234 and 765 add up to 999. A check with a calculator will also show that 234,765 is divisible by 999 without any remainder.
Is this a coincidence?

A certain shape of tile can be used to cover either of these shapes without overlapping and without leaving any gaps.

What shape is the tile?

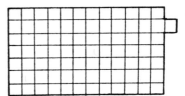

In the figure three rods have been arranged so that each rod is at right angles to the other two. They are in space. They are not necessarily touching each other.

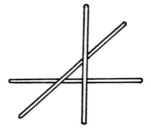

(a) How can 6 rods be arranged so that each rod is at right angles to 3 of the others?

(b) How can 6 rods be arranged so that each rod is at right angles to one of the others and at 60 degrees to the other 4 rods?

CROSS'S THEOREM

This neat theorem was discovered by a schoolboy, David Cross.

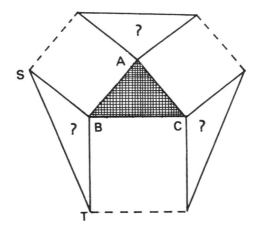

Squares have been drawn on the sides of an arbitrary triangle ABC, and the free corners joined to make three more triangles.

The areas of these new triangles are all equal to the area of the original triangle. Why?

101

Here are 9 spaces, lying 3 by 3 on 9 lines. Is it possible to place the numbers 1 to 9 in the spaces, one each, so that the sum of the numbers in each of the rows is the same?

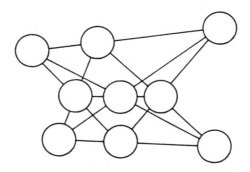

102

1 3 9 27 81 243 729 2187 6561 19683 59049 177147

What is the sum of this sequence? If the sequence is continued far enough, its sum can be as large as we please, so you are only asked to sum it to 177147, without, of course, doing a boring addition sum.

103

There are only three tessellations possible using tiles which are regular polygons

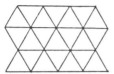
Equilateral Triangles

Squares

Hexagons

However, there are infinitely many tessellations made up of a single tile, where the tile is irregular in shape.

Show how you can make a tessellation, using a single tile which is an irregular 7 sided polygon. Then 8. Then n.

104

What is the largest set of whole numbers less than 100, such that no number in the set is the sum of two other numbers in the set? What is the largest set, so that no number is the difference of two others?

105

What is the largest set of whole numbers less than 100, such that no number in the set is a product of two other numbers in the set?

106

Place the numbers 1 to 16, once each in these squares so that the total of all the differences between any pair of adjacent numbers is as large as possible.

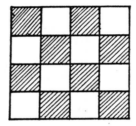

Horizontal and vertical differences are included, so there are 24 altogether.

107

Most of the largest prime numbers which are known are what are called 'Mersenne Primes'. These are numbers in the form

$$2^p - 1 \text{ where p is an integer.}$$

A newspaper, reporting the discovery of the largest prime number so far, said that p = 131,049. A second newspaper said p = 132,049.
Assuming that one of these is correct and that the other is a typographical error, which would you opt for, and why?

A straight line moves from the vertex of this triangle to the base (until it disappears at the right hand corner), always remaining at the same angle to the base. What is its average length during its journey?

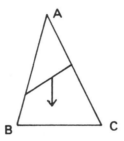

How large can the difference between two numbers be if they are not whole numbers and there is no whole number between them?

Find a sequence of numbers in which each number is one more than the sum of all previous numbers in the sequence, and only one of the numbers is not a multiple of 5.

Four-digit numbers have a curious property.
13 divides 1417, and also divides 417,001. It is also true
that 13 divides 8463 and 463,008, and also 7202 and
202,007 . . . .

It is easy to check that it works for any four-digit number
which divides by 13.
The number 13 in this trick could be replaced by either of
two other prime numbers. What are they?

These four pieces will fit together to make a simple
shape. What is it?

113

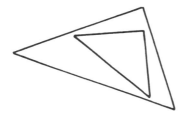

I have two triangles. The longest side, the middle side and the shortest side of the first are all shorter than the longest side, the middle side and the shortest side of the second respectively.

Is it necessarily true that the 'smaller' triangle is always able to fit inside the larger?

114

The sum of two numbers is equal to their product and both the sum and product are as small as possible.

What are the numbers?

Imagine that this tessellation of hexagons goes on for ever in all directions

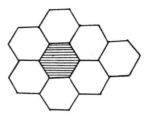

Then imagine that the hexagons begin to drift apart from each other in a completely symmetrical way.

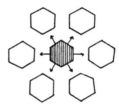

The gaps between the hexagons can then be filled with squares and equilateral triangles.

Can you devise a tessellation which contains twice as many triangles and three times as many squares as hexagons?

Can you devise a tessellation which contains twice as many triangles and six times as many squares as hexagons?

116

This ribbon has been wrapped around the cube so that it passes directly over the middle points of six edges. The loop of ribbon has no slack, and its material will not stretch. Is it possible to move it on the cube except by sliding it along its own length?

Will it move sideways?

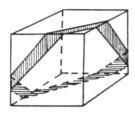

117

Rearrange all these words to make a true sentence, adding punctuation where necessary.

HAVE	DIFFERENCE	FACTOR
DO	THEIR	SUM
SAME	THE	THEN
SO	NUMBERS	TWO
AND	IF	THEIR

This problem is all about 7 x 10 rectangles.

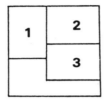
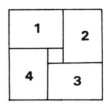

The smallest square into which three of these rectangles fit is 17 x 17. This square will also take 4.

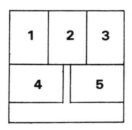
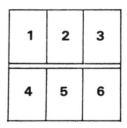

Curiously, the smallest square which will take 5 rectangles is 21 x 21, and it will also take 6.

What is the smallest odd number of rectangles such that the smallest square into which they will fit, will *NOT* take an extra rectangle?
Ignoring of course the answer 1.

March					
Mon		3	10	17	24	31
Tue		4	11	18	25
Wed		5	12	19	26
Thu		6	13	20	27
Fri		7	14	21	28
Sat	1	8	15	22	29
Sun	2	9	16	23	30

This calendar is for March 1986. When could it have been used before, and when will it be used again?

Using this calendar, what day of the week will the next February 29th be?

This problem is supposed to have been invented by Sir Issac Newton:

"If 12 oxen will eat $3\frac{1}{2}$ acres of grass in 4 weeks, and 21 oxen will eat 10 acres of grass in 9 weeks, how many oxen will eat 24 acres in 18 weeks, if the grass always grows at a uniform rate".

Two polyhedron posers

(1) Why is it impossible for a polyhedron to have 7 triangular faces?

(2) How many polyhedra have 8 equilateral triangle faces?

122

Equal lengths of fine wire are bent in pairs into a series of semi circles.

ONE

TWO

THREE

When the two pieces with the same number of semicircles are placed on top of each other they form a series of circles.

Investigate the total area enclosed for different numbers of circles in terms of the area of the single circle.

123

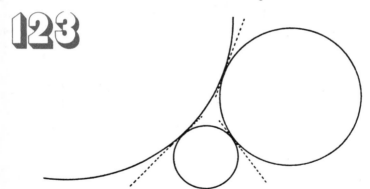

Here are three circles touching each other. Between each pair of circles is a line which touches each of the circles at the point where they meet.

If these three lines are extended inwards, they will meet at one point. Why?

Hints for Solutions

Ideas and suggestions which can help, but which do not give away the solution.

HINTS FOR SOLUTIONS

1. B and F must both end in zero.
2. If you join one vertex to the mid-point of the opposite side of a triangle, it will divide it into two triangles of equal area.
3. No hint.
4. This new design of board has no special centre. All spaces bear the same relationship to all other spaces.
5. Simplify P + (Q x R) = (P +Q) x (P+ R).
6. The shape must be regular. What regular shape has 8 vertices?
7. Try it and see.
8. Think of B and the tiny central region as one piece.
9. Not one letter is repeated in either message.
10. Think of fairly regular 5, 10 or 20 sided shapes.
11. Draw vertical and horizontal lines through T.
12. Think of travelling between the two points by first going horizontally, then vertically.
13. Sketch and experiment.
14. Divide it by lines through the centre and then make adjustments.
15. Base the solution on symmetry and equal sized pieces.
16. Give meaning to the nonsense words. For example squifm = "knife", norit = "sharp", meghim="made in Aberdeen".
17. Think of another first line that could lead to the same second line.
18. Imagine how far uphill a fly would have to climb if it walked along the parallel edges of the frame.
19. Take the first two numbers away from the third.
20. A cylinder can be unrolled to make a rectangle.
21. Look at row 4.
22. Make a cardboard cylinder and experiment.
23. Imagine a line through X which rotates steadily. Think of the lengths of the two segments either side of X.
24. 200.
25. If the digits in the first row are x and y then the value of the number is $10 x + y$.
26. Mathematical vocabulary.
27. Experiment with several drawings.
28. The surface of a cone can be unwrapped and spread out.
29. Divide the first shape into unit squares.
30. Three points define a plane. All other points in the plane are combinations of those co-ordinates. For example: It is true that
$2 x (1,2,3) + 1 x (3,5,1) +1 x (10,15,4) = (15,24,11)$.
31. If each point is joined to four other equidistant points, the points become vertices where four regions or vertices meet.
32. Study the pattern along the perimeter.
33. A pentagon must have five other faces joined to it and a hexagon must have six.
34. Think of the properties of the number 6.
35. Consider the remainders when powers of 17 are divided by 7.
36. Look round the kitchen.
37. Consider the point of balance of each rectangle separately.
38. You cannot use $1/_2$ because it is too big. Try $1/_4$. The $1/_8$ would take you over, so try $1/_{16}$ and so on.
39. Consider the diagonal PR.
40. What is the chance that the first card is black? The second?
41. The values of a and b must be very simple.

HINTS FOR SOLUTIONS

42. The 5 digit answer can be written as the product of the 2 digit and 3 digit number in only one way.

43. $5 = 1^2 + 2^2$: $29 = 2^2 + 5^2$.

44. Divide each number by their highest common factor. Then look for a difference of 1 between their multiples.

45. Similar triangles.

46. Experiment on sketched axes.

47. The sum of consecutive factorials starts with 1.

48. Measure the distance between the cars on the corner and on the straight.

49. At least three of the numbers have factors which are not repeated.

50. Consider edges that cross each other.

51. Imagine the shapes fitted together.

52. Cut a parallel strip off one side of the ladder so that the top rung is reduced to zero length.

53. Trial and error.

54. Try it on a model.

55. There is a connection with the number 7.

56. The average of the average of 2,4,7, and 3,6,8 is the same as the average of 2,4,7,3,6,8. Experiment with different splits of these numbers.

57. The angle in a semi-circle is a right angle.

58. All four sides and all four angles need 8 measurements. Can you manage with less?

59. Trace and cut out the shapes. Then compare lengths to look for possibilities.

60. The polyhedra are both regular.

61. The volume of a pyramid is equal to one third of the area of the base times the height. A tetrahedron is a pyramid.

62. All points which are the same distance from two points, lie on one straight line. All the points equidistant from two lines, lie on two straight lines.

63. Any prime which divides one of the numbers must divide the other also.

64. The value of p is irrelevant.

65. The strip ST is parallel to AB.

66. Consider how often you would pick a white counter from bag A or bag B if you performed the experiment a large number of times.

67. The ratio of a to b must be the same as the ratio of b to half a.

68. A tetrahedron is a triangular based pyramid.

69. No hint.

70. $1001 = 7 \times 11 \times 13$.

71. No hint.

72. If a is a root, then
$a^2 - 5a + 7 = 0$
If b is a root, then
$b^2 - 5b + 7 = 0$
Both of the statements are true at the same time.

73. Complete the diagram by continuing all lines until they meet.

74. Try drawing a strip parallel to one side and then dividing it up into equilateral triangles.

75. $\sqrt{5}$ is the length of the hypoteneuse of a right angled triangle of sides 1 and 2.

76. Imagine a plan view looking along a diagonal.

77. (a) The 'sticking out' piece must be repeated somewhere.
(b) How many units in each piece?

78. Roughly how many digits will x^7 and x^{13} contribute each?

79. (a) Think of the colour of the squares on which the knight lands.
(b) From which squares can the knight reach the corner squares?

80. Find the shortest distance across each shape, (its smallest diameter).

81. Where are the centres of circles which are equidistant from two points?

82. Try working backwards from one line to the previous line.

HINTS FOR SOLUTIONS

83. First find the centre of the square and then consider the movements along and up to reach each corner from the centre.

84. 7 x 142857 = 999999

85. Pick one pair of opposite faces to be marked with 1 and 8 and then study how the others can be arranged around them.

86. Find or make numbered counters. Then they can be moved as you play.

87. Make a tessellation of the two sizes of parallelogram to cover the plane. Then divide up the area in a different way.

88. Test the actual cost around 30, the point where the price per copy suddenly drops.

89. The condition means that the colours are spread out as much as possible.

90. Draw some possible positions. Then think in three dimensions.

91. The hint is in the heading.

92. Any quadrilateral can be tessellated.

93. The rate of flow of water is constant.

94. Make counters with the letters on and then move them and investigate.

95. Imagine that a third circle with the same radius is added, at right angles to the other two

96. (a) 'doubling'   (b) 'powers of two'.

97. 234,765 = 999 x 235.

98. The area of the smaller of these two shapes is 25, so the area of the tile must be a factor of this.

99. The rods do not necessarily have to touch each other, although they may do so.

100. Trace BST and try fitting it to ABC. This may suggest a solution.

101. If it is possible, then each row must add up to 15 as it does in an ordinary magic square.

102. The sum of the first three terms is 13 which is connected to the fourth term.

103. Start with a tessellation of squares or triangles.

104. The two problems are the same, but there are two solutions.

105. The square root of 100 is 10.

106. All the differences are between a shaded square and an unshaded square.

107. Check if both numbers for p appear to be prime.

108. Consider what happens before and after the line passes through B.

109. No hint.

110. Think of doubling.

111. The problem hinges around the number 1001.

112. No hint.

113. It is valuable to draw and cut out examples of the smaller triangle to see if it can always be fitted inside the larger.

114. 5 and $^5/_4$ have the same sum and product. So do 7 and $^7/_6$.

115. Imagine the spaces between the hexagons being filled with triangles and squares as they drift apart.

116. Would the ribbon have to get longer in order to move?

117. Start with 'IF'.

118. Experiment on squared paper. It is then easy to sketch the 7 x 10 rectangles accurately enough.

119. 364 divides exactly by 7. 365 leaves a remainder of 1. But there are leap years.

120. Focus on the amount of grass, call it G, by which each acre of grass increases each week. Find out how much 1 ox eats in one week in two different ways.

HINTS FOR SOLUTIONS

121. First poser: What is the connection between the number of edges of a polyhedron and the number of edges of its faces?

Second poser: The octahedron is not the only solution.

122. The area of a circle is equal to its radius multiplied by one half of the circumference.

123. The dotted lines are tangents.

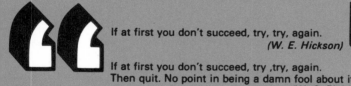

If at first you don't succeed, try, try, again.
(W. E. Hickson)

If at first you don't succeed, try ,try, again.
Then quit. No point in being a damn fool about it.
(W. C. Fields)

SOLUTIONS

The solutions are printed upside-down
to discourage all except the truly desperate.
See the quotations opposite.

form $a^3 - 1$ factorise into $(a - 1)(a^2 + a + 1)$ and so cannot be prime. We assume the other number is prime, and in fact it is. At the time of writing it is the second largest prime known.

108. Consider the instant when the line passes through B. Call the position it has reached X. The average length above BX is ½BX and so it also is below. The average length is thus one half of BX.

109. This is a simple example of a problem to which it seems there should be a straightforward answer, but there isn't! The difference can be as close to one as we like, but always a bit less. We cannot however name it, because whatever number we named, such as 0.999999999999, we could always find a slightly bigger difference, such as 0.999999999999999.

110. From the 2nd number, the sequence must simply double. Meeting the other conditions, the smallest answer is
$$4, 5, 10, 20, 40, 80, \ldots.$$

111. 7 or 11. The factors of 1001 are 7, 11, 13.

112. A block $8 \times 4 \times 3$.

113. Common sense might well suggest that it will always be possible to fit the smaller inside the larger, but this is not the case. Here is a counter example

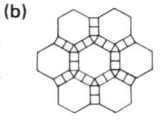

114. In general, numbers which have the same sum and product have the form

N and $\frac{N}{N-1}$ (Solve the equation $a + b = ab$).

The smallest value is for $N = 2$. The numbers are 2 and 2.

115. (a)   (b)

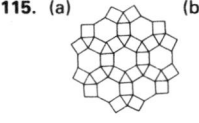

116. The ribbon can move in either direction as long as it remains parallel to itself.

117. "If two numbers have the same factor then so do their sum and their difference".

118. The smallest square to take 7 will also take 8, but the smallest to take 9 just fails to take 10.

119. 1975 ; 1998 ; A Monday (in 1988).

120. Each acre of grass is effectively increasing in size by a certain amount each week. Call it G.
Then 12 oxen would eat $3\frac{1}{2} + 3\frac{1}{2} \times G \times 4$ in four weeks.

1 ox in 1 week eats $\frac{7 + 28G}{2 \times 12 \times 4}$

And 21 oxen would eat $10 + 10 \times G \times 9$ in nine weeks.

1 ox in 1 week eats $\frac{10 + 90G}{21 \times 9}$

Equating these expressions $G = \frac{121}{1116}$

The number of oxen will be $37 \cdot 64$ — or 38 since parts of oxen do not eat!

121. (1) 7 triangular faces would have 21 edges, but each edge is where two faces meet, so the number must be even.
(2) Two, the octahedron and the polyhedron formed by gluing 3 tetrahedra together, face to face.

122. The area of a circle is its radius times one half of its circumference. In this problem the length of its wire is half the circumference of the circles. This is fixed. The total area is therefore inversely proportional to the number of circles. If the area of one circle is A, then of two it is $A/_2$, of three $A/_3$ and so on.

123. Tangents from any point to a circle are equal in length. The dotted lines are tangents and must therefore meet at a point which is equidistant from all three points of contact.

SOLUTIONS

92. Take any tessellation of quadrilaterals. Divide one up into four different shaped quadrilaterals and then repeat it in each one of the originals.

93. The same amount of water must pass each point of the column in the same time. As it falls, the water gathers speed. Hence the column must get narrower. The speed of the water at each point is inversely proportional to the area of the cross-section at the point.

94. There are 4 possible pieces in the left hand position, and for each one there are 3 arrangements of the right hand pieces, making 12 positions in all.
If we connect positions which can be reached from each other with lines, we get a diagram which starts like this.

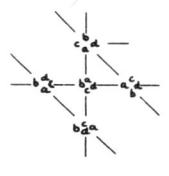

If we complete the network, we get a symmetrical polyhedron like this:

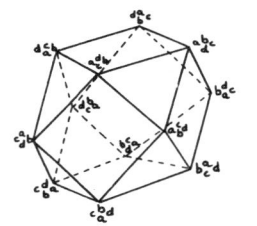

Any problem about the position of pieces can be solved from this polyhedron.

95. If you imagine the third circle at right angles to the other two, then AB is one of six equal steps which complete the circuit back to A again, all in the same

plane. AB is a side of a hexagon and is 10cm.

96. (a) 'Double and take away one', then double and add one'. It continues 85, 171, 341, ...
(b) The sums of two powers of 2 : 1 + 2 = 3, 1 + 4 = 5, 2 + 4 = 6, 1 + 8 = 9, ...
The next few terms are 17, 18, 20, 24

97. No. These properties always go together. Try to prove it.

98. 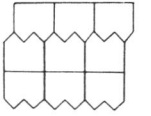 The tile will occupy 5 squares

99. (a) Three parallel rods are placed at right angles to another set of three parallel rods.
(b) Along the edges of a regular tetrahedron.

100. Rotate triangle BST about B until BT coincides with BC. Then ABS will be straight. The triangles ABC and BST are then equal because they have the same base and the same height.

101. No. These are at most two spaces not in line with any space. But 9 must not be in the same line as 8, 7 or 6. The total must be 15 and so it is impossible.

102. $(3 \times 177147 - 1) \div 2 = 265720$.

103. Start with a tessellation of triangles or squares and adjust one side until you have the required number of sides. A zig-zag adjustment is sufficient.

104. The solutions to both problems are the same. There are two different possibilities (1) 50 to 99 inclusive (2) all the odd numbers.

105. All the numbers from 10 to 99 inclusive.

106. Starting top left: 8, 12, 5, 9 : 11, 1, 16, 6 : 4, 15, 2, 13 : 10, 3, 14, 7.

107. The number 131,049 is divisible by 3 and so 2^p is a cube. Expressions of the

With $1 + \sqrt{5}$ and 2 draw a triangle as in the problem and you have an angle of 72°.

76. On a photograph the six edges would form a regular hexagon.

77.

78. x^{13} is roughly $(x^7)^2$ and squaring a number roughly doubles the number of digits. We would expect x^{13} to contribute roughly $\frac{2}{3}$ of the digits (say 25 or 26) and x^7 roughly $\frac{1}{3}$ (say 12 or 13).

A 25 digit number is of the order of 10^{24}

$\therefore x^{13} \doteqdot 10^{24}$ or $13 \log_{10}x \doteqdot 24$

$\therefore \log_{10}x \doteqdot 1.85$ and $x \doteqdot 70.17$

The answer is 71.

79. The knight moves from black to white and so it is impossible on a 25 squared board.

Joining the edges does help, because it is then possible to jump between squares of the same colour.

It is possible to visit each square once if you do not return to the starting point.

This is one solution: Reading L to R
3, 10, 21, 16, 5; 20, 15, 4, 11, 22; 9, 2, 25, 6, 17; 14, 19, 8, 23, 12; 1, 24, 13, 18, 7.

80. Divide the shortest diameter of each shape into four and draw lines at right angles at the $\frac{1}{4}$ and $\frac{3}{4}$ marks.

81. Choose one pair of points and draw the perpendicular bisector. Then draw the perpendicular bisector of the other pair. Where the two lines intersect is the centre of the circle. Find the radius by averaging the difference between the distances to one point of each pair.

82. No, the first line will not necessarily repeat, because a line may be preceded by either of several lines. For example C-A-C-B could be preceded by C-C-B-A or A-B-C-C or B-A-A-B. A pattern starting with C-C-B-A could go into a repeating loop from line 2 onwards.

83. The centre of the sqaure is (5,7) and the missing vertices will be (2,9) (which is 3 left and 2 up) and (8,5) (3 right and 2 down).

84. The product of a number and the number which repeats in the decimal representation of the number is always a sequence of 9s. For 7 digits we need 9,999,999.

But $9,999,999 = 9 \times 239 \times 4649$

The smallest number is $\frac{1}{239}$

85. There are 16 different arrangements, 768 for a dodecahedron.

86. No solution given.

87. Make a tessellation of the two sizes of parallelogram to cover the plane. Then divide up the area in a different way.

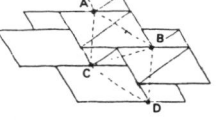

ABDC is the sum of the two parallelograms. ABC is the required area.

88. $25 \times 60p = £15.00$, $30 \times 50p = £15.00$. There is no point in ordering 25 to 29 copies.

89. Reading left to right, top to bottom
Y : R,G : G,Y,R : Y,R,G,Y : R,G,Y,R,G.

90. On a plane P would trace out two arcs of a circle. In space it would trace out the shape obtained by rotating the arc about the line AB. A sort of doughnut without a hole in the middle!

91. 1 (ONE) is the smallest number which uses three letters. 4 (FOUR) is the smallest which uses 4 letters. 3 (THREE) is the smallest which uses 5 letters and so on.

61. Imagine the box being cut in half vertically along AB. The tetrahedron is one third of what remains or one sixth of the original box.

Half the box is visible and half of each visible side is cut away. Therefore 3/4 of the weight remains.

62. One : Points equidistant from two given points lie on the perpendicular bisector. The three perpendicular bisectors meet at a single point.

Four : The internal and external bisectors of the angles between the lines meet at four points.

63. $p = 2$, $q = 4$ or vice versa.

64. $qr = q^r$ or $r = q^{r-1}$. Because powers increase so rapidly in size, the only solution is $q = r = 2$.

65. S traces the same shaped path as T, but the distance of AB to the left.

66. To avoid fractions in probability problems consider doing the experiment many times. Imagine 70 trials. Each bag will be chosen 35 times. From bag A a white will be chosen 14 times (2 out of 5). From bag B a white will be chosen 15 times (3 out of 7). Hence white would be chosen 29 times of which 14 would be from bag A. Hence the chance that a single white counter was from bag A was $^{14}/_{29}$.

67. $a : b$ must be $\sqrt{2} : 1$

68.

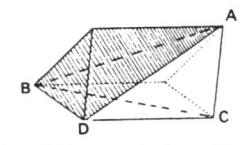

Slice off the tetrahedron ABD. Then make two more by cutting along ABC.

69.

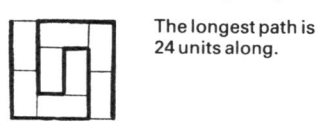

The longest path is 24 units along.

70. True: We prove it by supposing that it is false. Call the two numbers p and q. If pq is divisible by 1001, then it is divisible by 7. Hence either p or q is divisible by 7. But $p + q = 1001$ is also divisible by 7 and therefore if 7 divides one of the numbers, it divides both.

Similarly 11 and 13 must divide both numbers. Hence both p and q must be multiples of 1001. If so, they cannot add up to 1001. The statement cannot be false and therefore must be true.

71. Lay scissors on a flat surface pointing towards you. If the upper blade is on the right, then they are right handed.

72. If a and b both satisfy the equation
$$a^2 - 5a + 7 = 0$$
$$b^2 - 5b + 7 = 0$$
Subtracting
$$a^2 - b^2 - 5(a - b) = 0$$
$$(a - b)(a + b) - 5(a - b) = 0$$
Since the roots are not equal $a - b$ is not zero and we can divide by it. Hence $a + b = 5$ and we have the sum of the roots without knowing what they are.

73.

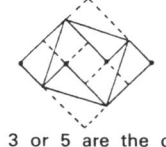

Complete the diagram. The vertices lie along the diagonal of the square.

74. 2, 3 or 5 are the only impossible numbers. A border strip can be divided into any odd number of equilateral triangles, from 3 on. In this example there are 7, making 8 in all. Hence any even number from 4 can be achieved. Any triangle can be cut into 4, increasing the number by 3. So any odd total from 4 on is possible.

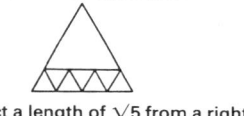

75. Construct a length of $\sqrt{5}$ from a right angled triangle of sides 1 and 2. Extend it by one unit to get $1 + \sqrt{5}$.

5. Join P to A and B and consider the ratios in the three similar triangles.
$$AX.XB = PX^2$$

6. Three pieces of information are enough. For example, one point on the line, (2 numbers), and the slope of the line, (one number).

7. $153 = 1^3 + 5^3 + 3^3 = 1! + 2! + 3!·+ 4! + 5! = \frac{1}{2}.17.18$ (The 17th triangular number).

8. The same number of cars are passing per minute, but they are only ¾ as far apart on the corner as on the straight. Hence the speed is approximately ¾ x $60 = 45$ kph.

9. At least 3 of the numbers are not perfect squares, and so have non-repeated factors. At least one of these factors must be greater than or equal to 5, and so cannot appear in any of the other numbers, and cannot be repeated in their product, which cannot be a square.

0.

Peter's definition would have been equivalent if he had added "and its edges do not cross each other". As the diagram shows, if the edges can cross, then his definition fails.

51. Together they make a 2x2x2 cube. Yes.

52. $\frac{1}{2} \times 50 + 10 = 35$.

53. $\sqrt{44} + \sqrt{70} = 14.999848$
The next best is
$$\sqrt{45} + \sqrt{28} = 11.9997066$$
Problem:
Of the 23 totals which are closest to a whole number, 19 are slightly less and only 4 are slightly more. Is there any reason for this lack of balance?

54.

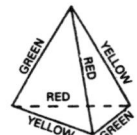

55. $142 + 857 = 999$: $14 + 28 + 57 = 99$

56. When the original two sets each contain the same number of numbers, or when both original sets have the same average.

57. Place the set square on the circle to obtain one diameter.

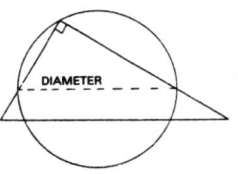

Then repeat it to obtain a second diameter. The centre is where they intersect.

58. 5 : There are many possibilities. (1) Four sides should be equal and one angle 90°. (2) Three angles are 90° and two adjacent sides equal. (3) Both halves of both diagonals are equal and they are at 90° to each other etc.

59.

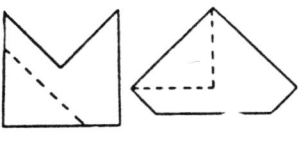

60. 30 : Perimeter and area of 5, 12, 13 triangle. The numbers less than and prime to 30 are the primes up to 29, excluding 2, 3 and 5. Both the icosahedron and the dodecahedron have 30 edges.

together as if it were a pattern of equilateral triangles.

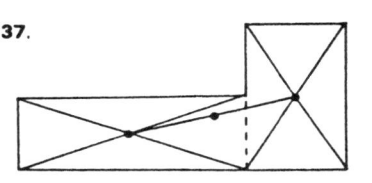

37.

The two rectangles are of equal area, so the point of balance is mid-way between the centres.

33. Some possibilities are: (1) A hexagonal pyramid (2) A tetrahedron with three vertices planed off (3) A polyhedra with 3 squares and four triangles (4) A polyhedra with one square and six triangles (5) A cuboid with one vertex planed off.

34. The numbers with this property are all multiples of 6. Since $6 = 3 + 2 + 1$, $12 = 6 + 4 + 2$, $18 = 9 + 6 + 3$ etc. All are obtained from

$$1 + \frac{1}{2} + \frac{1}{3} + \frac{1}{6}$$

There is no other way to express 1 as a sum of three reciprocals and so there are no other solutions.

35. This is a good example of the power of what is known as modular arithmetic. If 17 is divided by 7, it leaves a remainder of 3. 17^2 leaves remainder $3^2 = 9$, but 9 divides by 7 to leave 2. 17^6 leaves remainder $2^3 = 8$ which is equivalent to 1. 17^{18} leaves remainder $1^3 = 1$. 17^{19} leaves remainder 17 which is equivalent to 3 so we can be sure it does not divide exactly. Experiment with these ideas on smaller numbers until you are convinced.

36. Take a mug or cup and draw a loop around the handle.

38. The sum $\frac{1}{4} + \frac{1}{16} + \frac{1}{64} + \frac{1}{256} + \ldots = \frac{1}{3}$ and $\frac{1}{2} + \frac{1}{8} + \frac{1}{32} + \frac{1}{128} + \ldots = \frac{2}{3}$

39. Because the shorter strips are in the same proportion, say $1:x$ to the longer strips, Q will trace out the same shape as R but smaller – in the proportion $1:x$.

40. The chance the first card is black is $\frac{3}{6}$, the second $\frac{2}{5}$, the third $\frac{1}{4}$. The chance the fourth is red is 1, likewise the fifth and sixth.
The chance $= \frac{3}{6} \times \frac{2}{5} \times \frac{1}{4} \times 1 \times 1 \times 1 = \frac{1}{20}$.

41. $(a + b)^2 = a^2 + 2ab + b^2 = 1$
Since $a^2 + b^2 = 1$, $2ab = 0 \therefore$ either a or $b = 0$. Hence $a^5 + b^5 = 1$.

42. $271 \times 41 = 1111$.

43. $\sqrt{5}$ is the length of the hypotenuse of a right angled triangle, sides 1 and 2. $\sqrt{29}$ of sides 2 and 5. Also using right angled triangles:
$$35 = 6^2 - 1^2 \quad : \quad 33 = 7^2 - 4^2$$

44. Dividing through by the highest common factor reduces the problem to finding multiples of smaller numbers which differ by 1. Can this always be done? Yes, because the problem can always be reduced to one using smaller numbers still.
Consider 11 and 7.
Now $11 = 7 + 4$, so multiples of 11 can always be expressed in terms of multiples of 7 and 4. Likewise multiples of 7 can be expressed in terms of 4 and 3 which do differ by 1.
Now we can work backwards to find that $2 \times 11 - 3 \times 7 = 1$.

16. No.

17. $a + b + c = 0, -a + b + c = 0, a - b + c = 0$ and $a + b - c = 0$ all lead to the same equation, because squaring removes the negative signs. Therefore these four expressions are the factors of $2a^2b^2 + 2b^2c^2 + 2c^2a^2 - a^4 - b^4 - c^4$

18. $b = a + c$

19. $369,599 - 125,611 - 243,986 = 2$. Hence any common factor of all three must also divide into 2. The only possibilities are 2 and 1. Two of the numbers are odd, so there is no common factor except for 1.

20. Since the surface of the cylinder can be unrolled to make a rectangle, the problem reduces to this: can any rectangle be covered with squares? Yes, if the ratio of the sides is a fraction. No, if the ratio is irrational.

21. The 4th line can be written down directly from the first by applying the same rules, but not to each neighbouring pair. Apply them instead of the outside pair of each group of four.

    In the same way row 7 may be obtained from row 4, row 10 from row 7 and so on. Speeding up the process, row 10 may be obtained in a similar way directly from row 1. So may rows 28, 82, 244, ...

    Can you investigate why this is?

22. 6: The diagram shows the cylinder opened out into a rectangle.

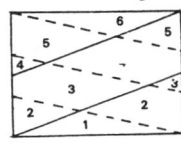

23.

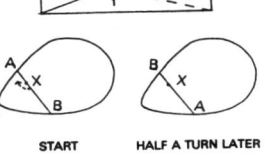

START   HALF A TURN LATER

Imagine a line AB, passing through X and which rotates about X. Let A initially be at one of the places where AX is as short as possible. Then BX > AX. Now rotate it through half a turn. A and B will interchange and AX > BX. At one point at least during the rotation AX = BX and X is the midpoint.

24. Choose a round number between the two numbers.
    $200 - 153 = 47$ and $482 - 200 = 282$
    $482 - 153 = 47 + 282 = 329$
    Subtraction becomes addition.

25. $11 + 27 + 12 + 17 = 67$

26. (1) No; Isoceles, Scalene. (2) Circle, Ellipse, Hyperbola, Parabola. (3) Tetrahedron, Octahedron, Hexahedron Dodecahedron, Icosahedron.
    Are there any other possibilities?

27. Experiment shows that the shape is an ellipse. It makes no difference if you start with an ellipse, of which a circle is a special case.

28. This problem depends on what you mean by an 'accurate square'. Unfold the cone so that it is flat and then draw the square on it. Then roll it up again.

29.

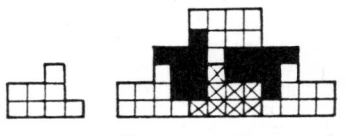

30. We try to see if we can spot that one of the points is a combination of the others
    $\frac{1}{2}(4,1,6) + \frac{1}{2}(5,2,8) + \frac{1}{2}(7,5,8) = (8,4,11)$

    So yes, they do lie in the same plane.

31. Each point becomes the vertex of a polyhedron where four faces and four equal edges meet. There is only one polyhedron with this property, the octahedron. So $n = 6$.

32. Each edge of the 'jagged triangle' is the same shape and so they will fit

1. A = 999, B = 10, C = 58, D = 981, E = 109, F = 90, G = 51, H = 908.

2. Join each vertex to the mid-point of the opposite sides. T is the point of intersection. The three triangles are equal by subtraction.

3. $9^2 - 4^2 = (9 + 4)(9 - 4) = 13 \times 5 = 65$, and so on. There are many patterns. One is that the difference between successive terms is double the difference between the squares.

4. Making the first O or X into a space on the board determines six spaces which are in the same line as the mark and two which are not. These two unconnected spaces are critical and the first player must win if he follows the best strategy. He must make his second move into one of the two unconnected spaces. The second player can only force a draw if he plays into one unconnected space and his opponent fails to play the into the other. Investigate.

5. This unusual equation will be true if and only if P,Q,R are three numbers whose sum is 1.

6. The points should lie on a cube. Each point is then a distance of one edge from its three nearest points. It is also a distance of $\sqrt{2}$ times an edge from three other points. The distances are equal in sets of three whether they are measured on the sphere or through it.

7.

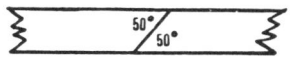

50°: The edge of the cube creases the strip, but does not alter the angle.

8.

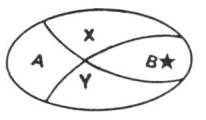

Leave out the vertical line. Then, since we are given A + X = B★ + Y and A + Y = B★ + X, X = Y and A = B★. The vertical line cuts off part of B★. Hence B is less than A.

9. The messages could be the same but do not have to be, 'I sat upon bed' or 'I can hold mug' are two possibilities.

10. A pyramid with a 10 sided base. A double pyramid with a five sided base. A prism with 10 sides which could be rolled. An icosahedron with the numbers 0 – 9 twice. Any others?

11. If the horizontal and vertical lines through T divide the long side into u and v and the short side into x and y, then $a^2 + b^2 = (u^2 + x^2) + (v^2 + y^2)$
$c^2 + d^2 = (v^2 + x^2) + (u^2 + y^2)$
Hence $a^2 + b^2 = c^2 + d^2$

12. Yes, (7,13): The horizontal distance between (x_1,y_1) and (x_2,y_2) is $x_1 - x_2$. *The vertical* distance is $y_1 - y_2$. The line passes through intermediate points only if $(x_1 - x_2)$ and $(y_1 - y_2)$ have a common factor. The line between (5,18) and (61,81) passes through six points.

13.

14.

15.

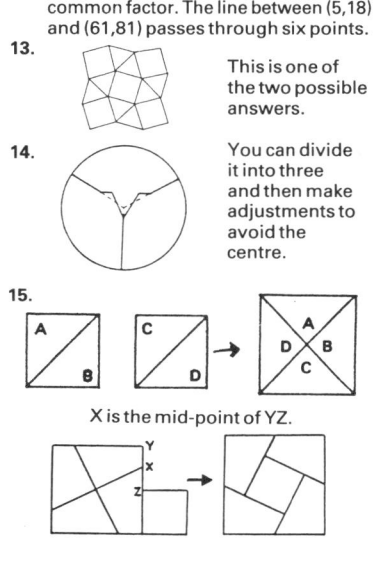

This is one of the two possible answers.

You can divide it into three and then make adjustments to avoid the centre.

X is the mid-point of YZ.

SOLUTIONS
AND SOME
FURTHER PROBLEMS
& INVESTIGATIONS